C000173134

Engineering and Construction Short Contract

The NEC3 Engineering and Construction Short Contract is an alternative to NEC3 Engineering and Construction Contract and is for use with contracts which do not require sophisticated management techniques, comprise straightforward work and impose only low risks on both the Employer and the Contractor

An NEC document

June 2005

OGC endorsement of NEC3

OGC advises public sector procurers that the form of contract used has to be selected according to the objectives of the project, aiming to satisfy the *Achieving Excellence in Construction* (AEC) principles.

This edition of the NEC (NEC3) complies fully with the AEC principles. OGC recommends the use of NEC3 by public sector construction procurers on their construction projects.

Office of Government Commerce

NEC is a division of Thomas Telford Ltd, which is a wholly owned subsidiary of the Institution of Civil Engineers (ICE), the owner and developer of the NEC.

The NEC is a family of standard contracts, each of which has these characteristics:

- Its use stimulates good management of the relationship between the two parties to the contract and, hence, of the work included in the contract.

- It can be used in a wide variety of commercial situations, for a wide variety of types of work and in any location.

- It is a clear and simple document – using language and a structure which are straightforward and easily understood.

NEC3 Engineering and Construction Short Contract is one of the NEC family and is consistent with all other NEC3 documents. Also available are the Engineering and Construction Short Contract Guidance Notes and Flow Charts.

ISBN (complete box set) 0 7277 3382 6
ISBN (this document) 0 7277 3372 9
ISBN (Engineering and Construction Short Contract Guidance Notes and Flow Charts) 0 7277 3373 7

First edition 1999
Second edition June 2005

Cover photo, Golden Jubilee Bridge, courtesy of City of Westminster

9 8 7 6 5 4 3 2

British Library Cataloguing in Publication Data for this publication is available from the British Library.

Typeset by Academic + Technical, Bristol

Printed and bound in Great Britain by Bell & Bain Limited, Glasgow, UK

ACKNOWLEDGEMENTS

The first edition of the NEC Engineering and Construction Short Contract was produced by the Institution of Civil Engineers through its NEC Panel. It was mainly drafted by Dr Martin Barnes, Tom Nicholson and Nigel Shaw based on work by Andrew Baird with the assistance of Peter Higgins and advice from Professor Phillip Capper of Masons Solicitors and David Maidment of Willis Corroon Construction Risks Ltd. Contributions were also made by Ross Hayes and Jon Broome of the University of Birmingham.

The second edition of the NEC Engineering and Construction Short Contract was mainly drafted by Professor J. G. Perry with the assistance of members of the NEC Panel. The Flow Charts were produced by Robert Gerrard with assistance from Ross Hayes and Tom Nicholson.

The original NEC was designed and drafted by Dr Martin Barnes then of Coopers and Lybrand with the assistance of Professor J. G. Perry then of The University of Birmingham, T. W. Weddell then of Travers Morgan Management, T. H. Nicholson, Consultant to the Institution of Civil Engineers, A. Norman then of the University of Manchester Institute of Science and Technology and P. A. Baird, then Corporate Contracts Consultant, Eskom, South Africa.

The members of the NEC Panel are:

    P. Higgins, BSc, CEng, FICE, FCIArb (Chairman)
    P. A. Baird, BSc, CEng, FICE, M(SA)ICE, MAPM
    M. Barnes, BSc(Eng), PhD, FREng, FICE, FCIOB, CCMI, ACIArb, MBCS, FInstCES, FAPM
    A. J. Bates, FRICS, MInstCES
    A. J. M. Blackler, BA, LLB(Cantab), MCIArb
    P. T. Cousins, BEng(Tech), DipArb, CEng, MICE, MCIArb, MCMI
    L. T. Eames, BSc, FRICS, FCIOB
    F. Forward, BA(Hons), DipArch, MSc(Const Law), RIBA, FCIArb
    Professor J. G. Perry, MEng, PhD, CEng, FICE, MAPM
    N. C. Shaw, FCIPS, CEng, MIMechE
    T. W. Weddell, BSc, CEng, DIC, FICE, FIStructE, ACIArb

NEC Consultant:

    R. A. Gerrard, BSc(Hons), MRICS, FCIArb, FInstCES

Secretariat:

    A. Cole, LLB, LLM, BL
    J. M. Hawkins, BA(Hons), MSc
    F. N. Vernon (Technical Adviser), BSc, CEng, MICE

Short Contract

A contract between ....

....

....

and ....

....

....

for ....

....

....

> **Notes about this contract are printed in boxes like this one. They are not part of the contract.**

contract data

conditions of contract

www.neccontract.com

Contract Data

contract data

conditions of contract

The *Employer* is

Name ....

Address ....

Telephone .... Fax ....

E-mail address ....

The *works* are ....

....

The *site* is ....

The *starting date* is ....

The *completion date* is ....

The *period for reply* is .... weeks.

The *defects date* is .... weeks after Completion.

The *defect correction period* is .... weeks.

The *delay damages* are .... per day.

The *assessment day* is the .... of each month.

The *retention* is .... %.

Does the United Kingdom Housing Grants, Construction and
Regeneration Act (1996) apply?   Yes / No (delete as appropriate)

The *Adjudicator* is

Name ....

Address ....

....

Telephone .... Fax ....

E-mail address ....

Contract Data

The interest rate on late payment is . . . . % per complete week of delay.

> Insert a rate only if a rate less than 0.5% per week of delay has been agreed.

The *Contractor* is not liable to the *Employer* for loss of or damage to the *Employer*'s

property in excess of . . . . for any one event.

The *Employer* provides this insurance

> Only enter details here if the *Employer* is to provide insurance.

. . . .

. . . .

The minimum amount of cover for the third insurance stated in the

Insurance Table is . . . .

The minimum amount of cover for the fourth insurance stated in the

Insurance Table is . . . .

The *Adjudicator nominating body* is . . . .

The *tribunal* is . . . .

If the *tribunal* is arbitration, the arbitration procedure is . . . .

The *conditions of contract* are the NEC3 Engineering and Construction Short Contract (June 2005) and the following additional conditions

> Only enter details here if additional conditions are required.

. . . .

. . . .

. . . .

. . . .

. . . .

. . . .

. . . .

. . . .

contract data

conditions of contract

Contract Data

The *Contractor*'s Offer

The *Contractor* is

Name ....

Address ....

....

Telephone .... Fax ....

E-mail address ....

The percentage for overheads and profit added to the Defined Cost for people is .... %.

The percentage for overheads and profit added to other Defined Cost is .... %.

The *Contractor* offers to Provide the Works in accordance with the *conditions of contract* for an amount to be determined in accordance with the *conditions of contract*.

The offered total of the Prices is ....

> **Enter the total of the Prices from the Price List.**

Signed on behalf of the *Contractor*

Name ....

Position ....

Signature .... Date ....

The *Employer*'s Acceptance

The *Employer* accepts the *Contractor*'s Offer to Provide the Works

Signed on behalf of the *Employer*

Name ....

Position ....

Signature .... Date ....

4

Contract Data

Price List

> Entries in the first four columns in this Price List are made either by the *Employer* or the tenderer.
>
> If the *Contractor* is to be paid an amount for the item which is not adjusted if the quantity of work in the item changes, the tenderer enters the amount in the Price column only; the Unit, Quantity and Rate columns being left blank.
>
> If the *Contractor* is to be paid an amount for the item of work which is the rate for the work multiplied by the quantity completed, the tenderer enters the rate which is then multiplied by the expected quantity to produce the Price, which is also entered.

Item number	Description	Unit	Quantity	Rate	Price
. . . .	. . . .	. . . .	. . . .	. . . .	. . . .
. . . .	. . . .	. . . .	. . . .	. . . .	. . . .
. . . .	. . . .	. . . .	. . . .	. . . .	. . . .
. . . .	. . . .	. . . .	. . . .	. . . .	. . . .
. . . .	. . . .	. . . .	. . . .	. . . .	. . . .
. . . .	. . . .	. . . .	. . . .	. . . .	. . . .
. . . .	. . . .	. . . .	. . . .	. . . .	. . . .
. . . .	. . . .	. . . .	. . . .	. . . .	. . . .
. . . .	. . . .	. . . .	. . . .	. . . .	. . . .
. . . .	. . . .	. . . .	. . . .	. . . .	. . . .
. . . .	. . . .	. . . .	. . . .	. . . .	. . . .
. . . .	. . . .	. . . .	. . . .	. . . .	. . . .
. . . .	. . . .	. . . .	. . . .	. . . .	. . . .
. . . .	. . . .	. . . .	. . . .	. . . .	. . . .
. . . .	. . . .	. . . .	. . . .	. . . .	. . . .
. . . .	. . . .	. . . .	. . . .	. . . .	. . . .

The total of the Prices [   ]

Contract Data

Works Information

> The Works Information should be a complete and precise statement of the *Employer*'s requirements. If it is incomplete or imprecise there is a risk that the *Contractor* will interpret it differently from the *Employer*'s intention. Information provided by the *Contractor* should be listed in the Works Information only if the *Employer* is satisfied that it is required, is part of a complete statement of the *Employer*'s requirements and is consistent with the other parts of the Works Information.

1 Description of the *works*

> Give a detailed description of what the *Contractor* is required to do and of any work the *Contractor* is to design.

....
....
....
....
....
....
....

2 Drawings

> List the drawings that apply to this contract.

Drawing number	Revision	Title
....	....	....
....	....	....
....	....	....
....	....	....
....	....	....
....	....	....
....	....	....

6

Contract Data

Works Information

3 Specifications

> List the specifications which apply to this contract.

Title	Date or revision	Tick if publicly available
. . . .	. . . .	. . . .
. . . .	. . . .	. . . .
. . . .	. . . .	. . . .
. . . .	. . . .	. . . .
. . . .	. . . .	. . . .
. . . .	. . . .	. . . .
. . . .	. . . .	. . . .
. . . .	. . . .	. . . .
. . . .	. . . .	. . . .
. . . .	. . . .	. . . .

4 Constraints on how the *Contractor* Provides the Works

> State any constraints on the sequence and timing of work and on the methods and conduct of work including the requirements for any work by the *Employer*.

7

© copyright nec 2005

Contract Data

Works Information

5 Requirements for the programme

State whether a programme is required and, if it is, state what form it is to be in, what information is to be shown on it, when it is to be submitted and when it is to be updated.

State what the use of the *works* is intended to be at their Completion as defined in Clause 11.2(1).

. . . .

. . . .

. . . .

. . . .

. . . .

. . . .

. . . .

6 Services and other things provided by the *Employer*

Describe what the *Employer* will provide, such as services (including water and electricity) and "free issue" Plant and Materials and equipment.

Item	Date by which it will be provided

8

Contract Data

Site Information

> Give information about the *site* such as the ground conditions and any other information which is likely to affect the *Contractor*'s work such as limitations on access and the position of adjacent structures.

....

....

....

....

....

....

....

....

....

....

....

....

....

....

....

....

....

....

....

....

....

....

....

contract data

conditions of contract

nec 3 Engineering and Construction Short Contract

CONDITIONS OF CONTRACT

1 General

Actions **10**

10.1 The *Employer* and the *Contractor* shall act as stated in this contract and in a spirit of mutual trust and co-operation.

Identified and defined **11**
terms 11.1 In the *conditions of contract*, terms identified in the Contract Data are in italics and defined terms have capital initials.

11.2 (1) Completion is when the *Contractor* has completed the *works* in accordance with the Works Information except for correcting notified Defects which do not prevent the *Employer* from using the *works* and others from doing their work.

(2) The Completion Date is the *completion date* unless later changed in accordance with this contract.

(3) A Defect is a part of the *works* which is not in accordance with the Works Information.

(4) The Defects Certificate is either a list of notified Defects which the *Contractor* has not corrected by the *defects date* or a statement that there are no such Defects.

(5) Defined Cost is the amount paid by the *Contractor* in Providing the Works (excluding any tax which the *Contractor* can recover) for

- people employed by the *Contractor*,
- Plant and Materials,
- work subcontracted by the *Contractor* and
- Equipment.

The amount for Equipment includes amounts paid for hired Equipment and an amount for the use of Equipment owned by the *Contractor* which is the amount the *Contractor* would have paid if the Equipment had been hired.

(6) Equipment is items provided by the *Contractor*, used by him to Provide the Works and not included in the *works*.

(7) The Parties are the *Employer* and the *Contractor*.

(8) Plant and Materials are items intended to be included in the *works*.

(9) The Price for Work Done to Date is the total of

- the Price for each lump sum item in the Price List which the *Contractor* has completed and
- where a quantity is stated for an item in the Price List, an amount calculated by multiplying the quantity which the *Contractor* has completed by the rate.

(10) The Prices are the amounts stated in the Price column of the Price List. Where a quantity is stated for an item in the Price List, the Price is calculated by multiplying the quantity by the rate.

contract data

conditions of contract

(11) To Provide the Works means to do the work necessary to complete the *works* in accordance with this contract and all incidental work, services and actions which this contract requires.

(12) Site Information is information which describes the *site* and its surroundings and is in the document called 'Site Information'.

(13) Works Information is information which either

- specifies and describes the *works* or
- states any constraints on how the *Contractor* Provides the Works

and is either

- in the document called 'Works Information' or
- in an instruction given in accordance with this contract.

Law 12

12.1 This contract is governed by the law of the country where the *site* is.

12.2 No change to this contract, unless provided for by the *conditions of contract*, has effect unless it has been agreed, confirmed in writing and signed by the Parties.

12.3 This contract is the entire agreement between the Parties.

Communications 13

13.1 Each communication which this contract requires has effect when it is received in writing at the last address notified by the recipient for receiving communications.

13.2 If this contract requires the *Employer* or the *Contractor* to reply to a communication, unless otherwise stated in this contract, he replies within the *period for reply*.

The *Employer*'s authority 14
and delegation

14.1 The *Contractor* obeys an instruction which is in accordance with this contract and is given to him by the *Employer*.

14.2 The *Employer* may give an instruction to the *Contractor* which changes the Works Information.

14.3 The *Employer*'s acceptance of a communication from the *Contractor* or of his work does not change the *Contractor*'s responsibility to Provide the Works or his liability for his design.

14.4 The *Employer*, after notifying the *Contractor*, may delegate any of the *Employer*'s actions and may cancel any delegation. A reference to an action of the *Employer* in this contract includes an action by his delegate.

Access to the *site* and 15
provision of services

15.1 The *Employer* allows access to and use of the *site* to the *Contractor* as necessary for the work included in this contract.

15.2 The *Employer* provides services and other things as stated in the Works Information.

Early warning 16

16.1 The *Contractor* and the *Employer* give an early warning by notifying the other as soon as either becomes aware of any matter which could

- increase the total of the Prices,
- delay Completion or
- impair the performance of the *works* in use.

The *Contractor* may give an early warning by notifying the *Employer* of any other matter which could increase his total cost. Early warning of a matter for which a compensation event has previously been notified is not required.

16.2 The *Contractor* and the *Employer* co-operate in making and considering proposals for how the effect of each matter which has been notified as an early warning can be avoided or reduced and deciding and recording actions to be taken.

2 The *Contractor*'s main responsibilities

Providing the Works **20**

20.1 The *Contractor* Provides the Works in accordance with the Works Information.

20.2 The *Contractor* does not start work which the *Contractor* has designed until the *Employer* has accepted that the design complies with the Works Information.

Subcontracting and people **21**

21.1 If the *Contractor* subcontracts work, he is responsible for Providing the Works as if he had not subcontracted.

21.2 This contract applies as if a subcontractor's employees and equipment were the *Contractor*'s.

21.3 The *Employer* may, having stated reasons, instruct the *Contractor* to remove an employee. The *Contractor* then arranges that, after one day, the employee has no further connection with the work included in this contract.

Access for the *Employer* **22**

22.1 The *Contractor* provides access for the *Employer* and others notified by the *Employer* to work being done for this contract and to stored Plant and Materials.

3 Time

Starting and Completion **30**

30.1 The *Contractor* does not start work until the *starting date* and does the work so that Completion is on or before the Completion Date.

30.2 The *Contractor* submits a forecast of the date of Completion to the *Employer* each week from the *starting date* until Completion.

30.3 The *Employer* decides the date of Completion and certifies it to the *Contractor* within one week of the date.

30.4 The *Employer* may instruct the *Contractor* to stop or not to start any work and may later instruct him to re-start or start it.

The programme **31**

31.1 The *Contractor* submits programmes to the *Employer* as stated in the Works Information.

4 Defects

Searching for and notifying Defects **40**

40.1 Until the *defects date,* the *Employer* may instruct the *Contractor* to search for a Defect.

40.2 The *Employer* may notify a Defect to the *Contractor* at any time before the *defects date.*

Correcting Defects **41**

41.1 The *Contractor* corrects a Defect whether or not the *Employer* notifies him of it.

41.2 Before Completion, the *Contractor* corrects a notified Defect before it would prevent the *Employer* or others from doing their work.

41.3 After Completion, the *Contractor* corrects a notified Defect before the end of the *defect correction period.* This period begins at the later of Completion and when the Defect is notified.

41.4 The *Employer* issues the Defects Certificate to the *Contractor* at the later of the *defects date* and the end of the last *defect correction period.*

Uncorrected Defects **42**

42.1 If the *Contractor* has not corrected a notified Defect within its *defect correction period,* the *Employer* assesses the cost of having the Defect corrected by other people and the *Contractor* pays this amount.

Repairs **43**

43.1 Until the Defects Certificate has been issued and unless otherwise instructed by the *Employer,* the *Contractor* promptly replaces loss of and repairs damage to the *works,* Plant and Materials.

5 Payment

Assessing the amount due **50**

50.1 The *Contractor* assesses the amount due and, by each *assessment day,* applies to the *Employer* for payment. There is an *assessment day* in each month from the *starting date* until the month after the Defects Certificate has been issued.

50.2 The *Contractor*'s application for payment includes details of how the amount has been assessed. The first application for payment is for the amount due. Other applications are for the change in the amount due since the previous payment.

50.3 The amount due is

- the Price for Work Done to Date
- plus other amounts to be paid to the *Contractor* (including any tax which the law requires the *Employer* to pay to the *Contractor*)
- less amounts to be paid by or retained from the *Contractor.*

50.4 The *Employer* corrects any wrongly assessed amount due and notifies the *Contractor* of the correction before paying the *Contractor.*

50.5 The *Contractor* pays *delay damages* for each day from the Completion Date until Completion.

50.6 An amount is retained from the *Contractor* in the assessment of each amount due until Completion. This amount is the *retention* applied to the Price for Work Done to Date. The amount retained is halved in the first assessment made after Completion and remains at this amount until the *assessment day* after the Defects Certificate is issued. No amount is retained in the assessment made after the Defects Certificate has been issued.

50.7 If the *Employer* requires a programme to be submitted, one quarter of the Price for Work Done to Date is retained in assessments of the amount due until the *Contractor* has submitted a first programme to the *Employer* showing the information which the Works Information requires.

Payment 51

51.1 The *Employer* pays within three weeks after the next *assessment day* which follows receipt of an application for payment by the *Contractor*.

51.2 Interest is paid if a payment is late or includes a correction of an earlier payment. Interest is assessed from the date by which the correct payment should have been made until the date when it is paid. Interest is calculated at the rate stated in the Contract Data or, if none is stated, at 0.5% of the delayed amount per complete week of delay.

6 Compensation events

Compensation events 60

60.1 The following are compensation events.

(1) The *Employer* gives an instruction changing the Works Information unless the change is in order to make a Defect acceptable.

(2) The *Employer* does not allow access to and use of the *site* to the *Contractor* as necessary for the work included in this contract.

(3) The *Employer* does not provide something which he is to provide by the date for providing it stated in this contract.

(4) The *Employer* gives an instruction to stop or not to start any work.

(5) The *Employer* does not work within the conditions stated in the Works Information.

(6) The *Employer* does not reply to a communication from the *Contractor* within the period required by this contract.

(7) The *Employer* changes a decision which he has previously communicated to the *Contractor*.

(8) The *Employer* instructs the *Contractor* to search for a Defect and no Defect is found.

(9) The *Contractor* encounters physical conditions which

- are within the *site*,
- are not weather conditions and
- an experienced contractor would have judged, at the date of the *Contractor*'s Offer, to have such a small chance of occurring that it would have been unreasonable to have allowed for them.

Only the difference between the physical conditions encountered and those for which it would have been reasonable to have allowed is taken into account in assessing a compensation event.

contract data

conditions of contract

(10) The *Contractor* is prevented by weather from carrying out all work on the *site* for periods of time, each at least one full working day, which are in total more than one seventh of the total number of days between the *starting date* and the Completion Date. In assessing this event, only the working days which exceed this limit and on which work is prevented by no other cause are taken into account.

(11) The *Employer* notifies a correction to an assumption which he has stated about a compensation event.

(12) An event which

- stops the *Contractor* completing the *works* or
- stops the *Contractor* completing the *works* by the Completion Date

and which

- neither Party could prevent,
- an experienced contractor would have judged at the date of the *Contractor*'s Offer to have such a small chance of occurring that it would have been unreasonable for him to have allowed for it and
- is not one of the other compensation events stated in this contract.

(13) A difference between the final total quantity of work done and the quantity stated for an item in the Price List.

(14) A loss of or damage to the *works*, Plant and Materials which

- is not the fault or responsibility of the *Contractor* or
- could not have been prevented by any reasonable action of the *Contractor*.

60.2 In judging the physical conditions for the purposes of assessing any compensation event, the *Contractor* is assumed to have taken into account

- the Site Information,
- publicly available information referred to in the Site Information,
- information obtainable from a visual inspection of the *site* and
- other information which an experienced contractor could reasonably be expected to have or to obtain.

Notifying compensation events **61**

61.1 The *Contractor* notifies the *Employer* of an event which has happened or which he expects to happen as a compensation event if

- the *Contractor* believes that the event is a compensation event and
- the *Employer* has not notified the event to the *Contractor*.

If the *Contractor* does not notify a compensation event within eight weeks of becoming aware of the event he is not entitled to a change in the Prices or Completion Date unless the event arises from an instruction of the *Employer*.

61.2 If the *Employer* decides that an event notified by the *Contractor*

- arises from a fault of the *Contractor*,
- has not happened and is not expected to happen,
- has no effect upon the Defined Cost or upon Completion or
- is not one of the compensation events stated in this contract,

he notifies the *Contractor* of his decision that the Prices and the Completion Date are not to be changed.

If the *Employer* decides otherwise, he instructs the *Contractor* to submit a quotation for the event. The *Employer* notifies the decision to the *Contractor* or instructs the *Contractor* to submit a quotation within one week of the *Contractor*'s notification to the *Employer* of the event.

61.3 If the *Employer* decides that the *Contractor* did not give an early warning of the event which the *Contractor* could have given, the *Employer* notifies that decision to the *Contractor* when instructing the *Contractor* to submit a quotation.

	61.4 If the *Employer* decides that the effects of a compensation event are too uncertain to be forecast reasonably, the *Employer* states assumptions about the event when instructing the *Contractor* to submit a quotation. Assessment of the event is based on these assumptions. If any of them is later found to have been wrong, the *Employer* notifies a correction.
	61.5 A compensation event is not notified after the *defects date*.

Quotations for **62**
compensation events 62.1   A quotation for a compensation event comprises proposed changes to the Prices or rates and any delay to the Completion Date assessed by the *Contractor*. The *Contractor* submits details of his assessment with each quotation. The *Contractor* submits a quotation within two weeks of being instructed to do so by the *Employer* or, if no such instruction is received, within two weeks of the notification of a compensation event.

62.2   The *Employer* may instruct the *Contractor* to submit a quotation for a proposed instruction or a proposed changed decision. The *Contractor* does not put a proposed instruction or a proposed changed decision into effect.

62.3   The *Employer* replies within two weeks of the *Contractor*'s submission.

For a proposed instruction or proposed changed decision, the *Employer*'s reply is

- notification that the proposed instruction will not be given or the proposed changed decision will not be made,
- notification of the instruction or changed decision as a compensation event and acceptance of the quotation or
- notification of the instruction or changed decision as a compensation event and notification that the *Employer* does not agree with the quotation.

For other compensation events, the *Employer*'s reply is

- acceptance of the quotation or
- notification that the *Employer* does not agree with the quotation.

62.4   If the *Employer* does not agree with the quotation, the *Contractor* may submit a revised quotation within two weeks of the *Employer*'s reply. If the *Employer* does not agree with the revised quotation or if none is received, the *Employer* assesses the compensation event and notifies the assessment.

62.5   After discussing with the *Contractor* different ways of dealing with the compensation event which are practicable, the *Employer* may instruct the *Contractor* to submit alternative quotations for a compensation event.

Assessing compensation **63**
events 63.1   For a compensation event which only affects the quantities of work shown in the Price List, the change to the Prices is assessed by multiplying the changed quantities of work by the appropriate rates in the Price List.

63.2   For other compensation events, the changes to the Prices are assessed by forecasting the effect of a compensation event upon the Defined Cost or, if the compensation event has already occurred, the assessment is based upon the Defined Cost due to the event which the *Contractor* has incurred. Effects on Defined Cost are assessed separately for

- people employed by the *Contractor*,
- Plant and Materials,
- work subcontracted by the *Contractor* and
- Equipment.

The *Contractor* shows how each of these effects is built up in each quotation for a compensation event. The percentages for overheads and profit stated in the *Contractor*'s Offer are applied to the assessed effect of the event on the Defined Cost.

contract data

conditions of contract

63.3 The effects of compensation events upon the Defined Cost are assessed at open market or competitively tendered prices with deductions for all discounts, rebates and taxes which can be recovered. The following are deducted from the Defined Cost for the assessment of compensation events

- the cost of events for which this contract requires the *Contractor* to insure and
- other costs paid to the *Contractor* by insurers.

63.4 A delay to the Completion Date is assessed as the length of time that, due to the compensation event, Completion is forecast to be delayed.

63.5 If the *Employer* has decided and notified the *Contractor* that the *Contractor* did not give an early warning of a compensation event which an experienced contractor could have given, the event is assessed as if the *Contractor* had given early warning.

63.6 Assessment of the effect of a compensation event includes risk allowances for cost and time for matters which are at the *Contractor*'s risk under this contract.

63.7 Assessments are based on the assumptions that the *Contractor* reacts competently and promptly to the compensation event and that any additional cost and time due to the event are reasonably incurred.

63.8 A compensation event which is an instruction to change the Works Information in order to resolve an ambiguity or inconsistency is assessed as if the Prices and the Completion Date were for the interpretation most favourable to the Party which did not provide the Works Information.

63.9 The assessment of a compensation event is not revised if a forecast upon which it is based is shown by later recorded information to have been wrong.

7 Title

Objects and materials within the *site* **70**

70.1 The *Contractor* has no title to an object of value or of historical or other interest within the *site*. The *Contractor* does not move such an object unless instructed to do so by the *Employer*.

70.2 The *Contractor* has title to materials from excavation and demolition only as stated in the Works Information.

8 Indemnity, insurance and liability

Limitation of liability **80**

80.1 For any one event, the liability of the *Contractor* to the *Employer* for loss of or damage to the *Employer*'s property is limited to the amount stated in the Contract Data. The *Contractor* is not liable to the *Employer* for the *Employer*'s indirect or consequential loss except as provided for in the *conditions of contract*. Exclusion or limitation of liability applies in contract, tort or delict and otherwise and to the maximum extent permitted in law.

Indemnities **81**

81.1 The *Employer* indemnifies the *Contractor* against claims, proceedings, compensation and costs payable which are the unavoidable result of the *works* or of Providing the Works or which arise from

- fault,
- negligence,
- breach of statutory duty,
- infringement of an intellectual property or
- interference with a legal right

by the *Employer* or by a person employed by or contracted to the *Employer* except the *Contractor*.

81.2 The *Contractor* indemnifies the *Employer* against other

- losses and claims in respect of
  - death of or injury to a person and
  - loss of and damage to property (other than the *works*, Plant and Materials) and
- claims, proceedings, compensation and costs payable arising from or in connection with the *Contractor*'s Providing the Works.

81.3 The liability of one Party to indemnify the other is reduced to the extent that events which are the other Party's responsibility contributed to the losses, claims, proceedings, compensation and costs.

Insurance cover **82**

82.1 The *Contractor* provides, in the joint names of the Parties and from the *starting date*, the insurances stated in the Insurance Table. The *Contractor* does not provide an insurance which the *Employer* is to provide as stated in the Contract Data.

INSURANCE TABLE

Insurance against	Minimum amount of cover or minimum limit of indemnity	Cover provided until
Loss of or damage to the *works*	The replacement cost	The *Employer*'s certificate of Completion has been issued
Loss of or damage to Equipment, Plant and Materials	The replacement cost	The Defects Certificate has been issued
The *Contractor*'s liability for loss of or damage to property (except the *works*, Plant and Materials and Equipment) and for bodily injury to or death of a person (not an employee of the *Contractor*) arising from or in connection with the *Contractor*'s Providing the Works	The amount stated in the Contract Data for any one event with cross liability so that the insurance applies to the Parties separately	
Liability for death of or bodily injury to employees of the *Contractor* arising out of and in the course of their employment in connection with this contract	The greater of the amount required by the applicable law and the amount stated in the Contract Data for any one event	

contract data

conditions of contract

9 Termination and dispute resolution

Termination and reasons for termination **90**

90.1 If either Party wishes to terminate the *Contractor*'s obligation to Provide the Works, he notifies the other Party giving details of his reason for terminating. The *Employer* issues a termination certificate promptly if the reason complies with this contract. After a termination certificate has been issued, the *Contractor* does no further work necessary to Provide the Works.

90.2 Either Party may terminate if the other Party has become insolvent or its equivalent (Reason 1).

90.3 The *Employer* may terminate if the *Employer* has notified the *Contractor* that the *Contractor* has defaulted in one of the following ways and the *Contractor* has not stopped defaulting within two weeks of the notification.

- Substantially failed to comply with this contract (Reason 2).
- Substantially hindered the *Employer* (Reason 3).
- Substantially broken a health or safety regulation (Reason 4).

The *Employer* may terminate for any other reason (Reason 5).

90.4 The *Contractor* may terminate if

- the *Employer* has not made a payment within ten weeks of the *assessment day* which followed receipt of the *Contractor*'s application for it (Reason 6) or
- the *Employer* has instructed the *Contractor* to stop or not to start any substantial work or all work for a reason which is not the *Contractor*'s fault and an instruction allowing the work to re-start or start has not been given within eight weeks (Reason 7).

90.5 The *Employer* may terminate if an event which the Parties could not reasonably prevent has substantially affected the *Contractor*'s work for a continuous period of more than thirteen weeks (Reason 8).

Procedures on termination **91**

91.1 On termination, the *Employer* may complete the *works* himself or employ other people to do so. The *Contractor* leaves the *site* and removes the Equipment.

Payment on termination **92**

92.1 The amount due on termination includes

- an amount due assessed as for normal payments,
- the cost of Plant and Materials provided by the *Contractor* which are on the *site* or of which the *Contractor* has to accept delivery and
- any amounts retained by the *Employer*.

92.2 If the *Employer* terminates for Reason 1, 2, 3 or 4, the amount due on termination also includes a deduction of the forecast additional cost to the *Employer* of completing the *works*.

92.3 If the *Contractor* terminates for Reason 1, 6 or 7 or if the *Employer* terminates for Reason 5, the amount due on termination also includes 5% of any excess of a forecast of the amount due at Completion had there been no termination over the amount due on termination assessed as for normal payments.

Dispute resolution **93**

93.1 A dispute arising under or in connection with this contract is referred to and decided by the *Adjudicator*.

The *Adjudicator* 93.2 (1) The Parties appoint the *Adjudicator* under the NEC Adjudicator's Contract current at the *starting date*. The *Adjudicator* acts impartially and decides the dispute as an independent adjudicator and not as an arbitrator.

contract data

conditions of contract

(2) If the *Adjudicator* is not identified in the Contract Data or if the *Adjudicator* resigns or is unable to act, the Parties choose a new adjudicator jointly. If the Parties have not chosen an adjudicator, either Party may ask the *Adjudicator nominating body* to choose one. The *Adjudicator nominating body* chooses an adjudicator within four days of the request. The chosen adjudicator becomes the *Adjudicator*.

(3) The *Adjudicator*, his employees and agents are not liable to the Parties for any action or failure to take action in an adjudication unless the action or failure to take action was in bad faith.

The adjudication **93.3** (1) A Party may refer a dispute to the *Adjudicator* if

- the Party notified the other Party of the dispute within four weeks of becoming aware of it and
- between two and four further weeks have passed since the notification.

If a disputed matter is not notified and referred within the times set out in this contract, neither Party may subsequently refer it to the *Adjudicator* or the *tribunal*.

(2) The Party referring the dispute to the *Adjudicator* includes with his referral information to be considered by the *Adjudicator*. Any more information is provided within two weeks of the referral. This period may be extended if the *Adjudicator* and the Parties agree.

(3) The *Adjudicator* may take the initiative in ascertaining the facts and the law related to the dispute. He may instruct a Party to take any other action which he considers necessary to reach his decision and to do so within a stated time.

(4) A communication between a Party and the *Adjudicator* is communicated to the other Party at the same time.

(5) If the *Adjudicator*'s decision includes assessment of additional cost or delay caused to the *Contractor,* he makes his assessment in the same way as a compensation event is assessed.

(6) The *Adjudicator* decides the dispute and notifies the Parties of his decision and his reasons within four weeks of the referral. This period may be extended by up to two weeks with the consent of the referring Party, or by any period agreed by the Parties.

If the *Adjudicator* does not notify his decision within the time allowed, either Party may act as if the *Adjudicator* has resigned.

(7) Unless and until the *Adjudicator* has notified the Parties of his decision, the Parties proceed as if the matter disputed was not disputed.

(8) The *Adjudicator*'s decision is binding on the Parties unless and until revised by the *tribunal* and is enforceable as a matter of contractual obligation between the Parties and not as an arbitral award. The *Adjudicator*'s decision is final and binding if neither Party has notified the other within the times required by this contract that he intends to refer the matter to the *tribunal*.

Review by the *tribunal* **93.4** A Party may refer a dispute to the *tribunal* if

- the Party is dissatisfied with the *Adjudicator*'s decision or
- the *Adjudicator* did not notify a decision within the time allowed and a new adjudicator has not been chosen,

except that neither Party may refer a dispute to the *tribunal* unless they have notified the other Party of their intention to do so not more than four weeks after the end of the time allowed for the *Adjudicator*'s decision.

If the United Kingdom Housing Grants, Construction and Regeneration Act 1996 applies to this contract, the following clause replaces clause 93.3(1) above.

The adjudication 94.1 A Party may issue to the other Party a notice of his intention to refer a dispute to adjudication at any time. He refers the dispute to the *Adjudicator* within one week of the notice.

nec 3 Engineering and Construction Short Contract

Index by clause numbers (main clause heads indicated by bold numbers). Terms in *italics* are identified in the Contract Data, and defined terms have capital initial letters.